MAC
ELEM

OSCAh vvILDE

The Picture of Dorian Gray

Retold by F. H. Cornish

MACMILLAN READERS

ELEMENTARY LEVEL

Founding Editor: John Milne

The Macmillan Readers provide a choice of enjoyable reading materials for learners of English. The series is published at six levels – Starter, Beginner, Elementary, Pre-intermediate, Intermediate and Upper.

Level control
Information, structure and vocabulary are controlled to suit the students' ability at each level.

The number of words at each level:

Starter	about 300 basic words
Beginner	about 600 basic words
Elementary	about 1100 basic words
Pre-intermediate	about 1400 basic words
Intermediate	about 1600 basic words
Upper	about 2200 basic words

Vocabulary
Some difficult words and phrases in this book are important for understanding the story. Some of these words are explained in the story and some are shown in the pictures. From Pre-intermediate level upwards, words are marked with a number like this: ...[3]. These words are explained in the Glossary at the end of the book.

Contents

A Note About the Author   *4*

PART ONE

1	Two Friends	*5*
2	A Very Beautiful Young Man	*9*
3	The Picture of Dorian Gray	*13*
4	Sibyl Vane	*16*
5	Brother and Sister	*20*
6	At the Theatre	*24*
7	Things Are Changing	*27*
8	Dorian Learns about Himself	*29*
9	Secrets	*33*

PART TWO

10	Two Friends	*37*
11	The Picture of Dorian Gray	*40*
12	Dorian Asks for Help	*45*
13	Prince Charming	*48*
14	Dorian Learns about Fear	*53*
15	A New Start for Dorian?	*57*

Points for Understanding   *61*

A Note About the Author

Oscar Wilde was born in Dublin, Ireland in 1854. He died in Paris in 1900. Many of the stories, plays and poems that Oscar Wilde wrote are still popular.

Stories: *The Picture of Dorian Gray, Lord Arthur Savile's Crime and Other Stories, The Happy Prince and Other Tales.*

Plays: *Lady Windermere's Fan, A Woman of No Importance, An Ideal Husband, The Importance of Being Earnest.*

Poems and Essays: *The Ballad of Reading Gaol, Ravenna, De Profundis.*

PART ONE

1

Two Friends

The curtains moved gently in the summer wind. The smell of flowers came in through the open window. And in the distance there was the faint noise of London traffic. It was very peaceful in the artist's studio.

Lord Henry Wotton was lying back in a large chair, smoking a cigarette. He was watching the blue smoke rise to the ceiling. And he was also watching his friend Basil Hallward, the artist. Basil was standing in front of a painting which was nearly finished. It was the portrait of a young man – a very beautiful young man.

Basil and Lord Henry were good friends. They had studied at Oxford University together. Now they were both about thirty years old. Basil worked very hard and he was a well-known artist. Lord Henry, who was called Harry by his friends, did not work at all. He was a rich man. He spent his money on expensive food and clothes, and on valuable books and paintings.

Lord Henry pointed towards the painting. 'That is the best portrait you have ever painted, Basil,' he said.

'You must show it in the best art gallery in London,' Lord Henry continued. 'Everybody must see it.'

'I am not going to show this picture in a gallery,' Basil replied.

'Not going to show it?' said Harry in surprise. 'You artists are silly people. You want to be famous. You become famous. Then you don't like being famous.

'Think, Basil. It's bad when people talk about you, but it's worse when they don't talk about you! Why won't you show the picture?'

'I know you will laugh at me, Harry,' answered Basil. 'But I can't show the picture because it shows too much of me. It is too much like me.'

'Nonsense,' said Harry. 'The picture does not look like you at all. You have black hair and a strong, intelligent face. But you are not beautiful, Basil. The young man in the portrait has blond hair and a pale face. And he is beautiful.'

'You don't understand me at all, Harry,' said Basil. 'I don't mean that I look like Dorian Gray.'

'Dorian Gray? Is that the young man's name?'

'Yes, that is his name. I didn't want to tell you.'

Basil stopped talking and went out of the door into the garden.

Harry laughed and followed him.

The two young men sat on a long wooden seat under a laurel tree. The summer wind moved through the shiny leaves.

Harry looked at his watch.

'I shall have to go soon, Basil,' he said, 'but first I want an answer to my question.'

'What question?' asked Basil.

'Why won't you show the picture of Dorian Gray in a gallery? What is the reason?'

'I told you the reason,' said Basil. 'It is too much like me.'

'But what do you mean?' asked Harry.

'I'm an artist,' said Basil, 'An artist paints pictures of other people. But I believe that an artist shows his own feelings in

6

every picture he paints. Each time I paint a picture, I show feelings that are inside me.

'I don't want people to look at the picture of Dorian Gray. I don't want them to find out about my feelings.'

Basil stopped speaking. Harry bent down and picked a small white flower from the grass.

'And what are your feelings, Basil? Tell me,' he said. He looked closely at the tiny flower.

At last Basil spoke again. 'I met Dorian at a party. It was Lady Brandon's party and a lot of people were there. Dorian and I saw each other at the same time. I felt afraid, but I don't know why. Then I felt that this person was very important to me. I felt that I had known him for a long time.

'Somebody introduced Dorian to me. Somebody made a joke and we both laughed. Suddenly Dorian and I were friends.'

'Well, laughter is the best beginning for a friendship,' said Harry. 'And it's the best ending for a friendship too.'

'Harry, you are never serious,' said Basil. 'Dorian is my closest friend. I see him every day. He is the most important thing in my life. He is more important to me than my work.'

'But I thought your work was the most important thing in your life, Basil,' said Harry.

'It is important. But I need Dorian. I am a better artist now that I know Dorian. Do you remember that picture of the landscape – the woods and fields? Everybody thought it was my best painting. Do you know why it was good? It was good because Dorian was there. He saw me paint it.

'Dorian has the power to make me a better artist. But I don't

7

want him to know this. I don't want anybody to know. So I can't show the painting in a gallery. It shows too much of me. It is too much like me.'

'I think you are wrong, Basil,' said Harry. 'Poets put their feelings into their poems. And they make money. So artists must put their feelings into their pictures. Then they can make money too.'

Then Harry thought of something else. 'You will get tired of this beautiful young man,' he said. 'One day his beauty will disappear and Dorian Gray won't be interesting any more.'

'No, Harry, that is not true. Don't talk like that!' said Basil. 'Dorian's beauty is not important to me. Dorian himself is important to me.'

'Dorian Gray must be an interesting young man!' said Harry. 'I want to meet him.'

'I don't want you to meet him,' replied Basil quickly.

'You don't want me to meet him?'

'No.'

Suddenly Basil's servant came out into the garden. 'Mr Dorian Gray is here, sir. He is in the studio,' he said.

'I will have to meet Dorian now,' said Harry, laughing.

'Please tell Mr Gray that I am coming,' said Basil to the servant.

Then Basil turned to Harry. He was upset and he spoke slowly to Harry.

'Please be careful, Harry,' he said. 'Dorian is beautiful and very young. You are never serious and you say strange things. Don't talk to him. Please don't try to influence him – to change him. Your influence would be bad. And I need him. I need him to help me with my work.'

'You're talking nonsense,' said Harry, smiling. 'Now, intro-
duce me to Dorian Gray.' He took hold of Basil's arm and led
him into the studio.

2

A Very Beautiful Young Man

The young man was sitting at the piano when Basil and Harry
came into the studio. He was turned away from them, looking at
a book of music. But he heard Basil's footsteps. Dorian spoke
immediately.

'Oh, Basil,' he said. 'Do you have to work today? I don't
want you to paint me today. I don't want a life-sized portrait
of myself.'

Then he turned and saw Harry. He stopped speaking. His
face became red. 'Oh, I didn't know you had a visitor.'

'Dorian,' said Basil, 'this is Lord Henry Wotton, a good
friend of mine. We went to university together. I have told
him that you like my painting of you. And now he won't
believe me.'

'Nonsense, Basil,' said Harry. 'I am very pleased to meet
you, Mr Gray.' Harry and Dorian shook hands.

Harry looked at Dorian Gray. Harry and Basil were both
about thirty years old. Dorian was much younger. He was
about twenty. And he was very beautiful. His hair was blond,
his face was pale and his eyes were bright blue.

Basil did not want Harry to talk to Dorian. 'Harry,' he said.
'I want to start painting now. Please will you go away?'

Harry did not want to go. 'Do you want me to go, Mr Gray?'

he asked. 'I will go if you want me to go. Or I will stay if you want me to stay.'

'Yes, do stay, Lord Henry,' answered Dorian.

'Mr Gray wants me to stay, Basil,' said Harry. 'You don't mind if I stay, do you?'

Basil wanted to please Dorian. 'No, of course I don't mind. Please stay, Harry,' he said.

'But,' Basil went on, 'you must not listen to Harry, Dorian. He is never serious and he says strange things. He changes people. He has a bad influence on people.

'Harry, sit down,' Basil continued. 'Dorian, come and stand over here. And please don't move around too much. I want to finish your portrait today.'

Basil started to paint. Harry sat in the comfortable chair and smoked a cigarette. There was silence for a few minutes.

Then Dorian spoke. 'Are you a bad influence on people, Lord Henry?' he asked. 'Do you make people change what they think and do?'

'I cannot be a bad influence or a good influence,' replied Harry. 'Because all influence is bad. It is bad to change a person. It is bad to give a person your thoughts and ideas.'

'Why?' asked Dorian.

'Everybody is different from everybody else,' answered Harry. 'You must not influence a person. You must not make a person the same as yourself.

'You must live your own life. You must do everything that you want to do. You must enjoy life – the good things and the evil things. You must not worry about what other people think.'

Dorian was confused. Harry was wrong to say these things. But Harry was clever. He had a thin face and clever, dark eyes. He had a beautiful, slow voice. Dorian liked listening to Harry

'Are you a bad influence on people, Lord Henry?'
Dorian asked.

speaking. Dorian had never met anyone like Harry before.

Harry did not speak again for a few minutes. He touched his small, pointed beard and he watched Dorian. Harry knew Dorian was thinking about the things he had said.

Basil continued painting. He had not listened to Harry talking.

Suddenly Dorian spoke. 'Basil, I'm tired of standing here,' he said. 'I'm too hot. I want to go out into the garden.'

'Oh, Dorian, I'm sorry,' replied Basil. 'When I am painting, I think of nothing else. Yes, you can go into the garden. Harry, you go with Dorian. I'll go on painting.'

Harry and Dorian went out into the garden. Dorian was thinking about the things Harry had said.

'Come and sit under the laurel tree,' said Harry. 'You must not get burned by the sun.'

So they sat on the long wooden seat. Dorian looked at the man who was sitting beside him. Harry was much older and cleverer than he was.

'Why mustn't I get sunburnt?' Dorian asked.

'Your skin is pale. You mustn't get sunburnt, because you must take care of your beauty,' said Harry. 'You are young and you are beautiful. And youth is very valuable.'

Dorian looked at Harry's long white hands and listened to Harry's beautiful, slow voice.

'One day you will be old,' said Harry. 'Your face will be wrinkled. You will be old and wrinkled and ugly. You will not be young, so you will not be beautiful any more. And it will be too late to do anything interesting and exciting.

'So, Mr Gray, you must enjoy life while you are young and beautiful. You must do everything you want to do. You must find out about life and people. You must not worry about what other people think.'

12

3

The Picture of Dorian Gray

Suddenly they heard Basil's voice. He sounded happy. 'I'm waiting,' he called. 'Come back into the studio, so I can continue painting. I'm painting very well today.'

Dorian stood without speaking while Basil painted. Harry sat in the armchair. The room was very quiet. The curtains moved gently and there was the sweet smell of flowers.

After a quarter of an hour, Basil stopped painting. He looked at Dorian for a long time. Then, for a long time, he looked at the picture.

'It is finished at last,' he cried. Then he picked up a paint-brush. He wrote his name in large red letters at the bottom of the picture.

Harry walked across the studio to look at the picture. It was a wonderful painting and it looked exactly like Dorian.

'Congratulations, Basil,' said Harry. 'It is the best portrait I have ever seen. Dorian, come and look at yourself.'

Dorian stood in front of the painting and looked at it. At first, he was pleased. He smiled at the painting. He smiled because he saw that he was a beautiful young man.

Then Dorian stopped smiling. Suddenly he remembered what Harry had said in the garden. Dorian Gray was young and beautiful now, but soon he would be old and wrinkled and ugly. He would not have blond hair or bright blue eyes. No one would want to look at him then.

Silently, Dorian stood in front of his picture.

Basil did not understand why the young man was silent. Basil was confused. 'Don't you like the picture?' he asked.

'Of course he likes it,' said Harry. 'It is a wonderful painting.

I want to buy it, Basil. I must buy it.'

'No, Harry,' replied Basil. 'I can't sell it. The picture belongs to Dorian. I have given it to him.'

'Dorian is very lucky,' said Harry.

Then Dorian spoke. 'It's very sad,' he whispered. 'I shall grow old and wrinkled and ugly. But this picture will always be young. This picture will never be older than it is today.'

'I wish that I could always be young. I wish that the picture could grow old instead of me. I would give anything and everything for this to happen. I would give my soul!'

'It would not be very nice for Basil if the painting grew old, Dorian,' said Harry, laughing.

'That's right,' said Basil, laughing too. 'I don't want that to happen. I don't want an old, ugly picture.'

But Dorian did not laugh. 'You care about your painting more than you care about me, Basil!' he shouted. 'You care about me now because I am young and beautiful. When I am old and ugly you won't care about me any more.

'It's not fair that the picture will always be beautiful,' Dorian said. 'I hate the picture. It will be young when I am old.'

Dorian ran to the big armchair. He laid his head on his arms and cried.

'Harry,' said Basil, angrily. 'This has happened because of you. This is your fault. I asked you not to talk to Dorian.'

Harry shook his head. 'No, Basil. It's not my fault. Dorian is learning about life.'

'Well,' said Basil, 'you are my two closest friends but you have made me hate my best painting. So I will destroy it.'

Basil picked up a knife from a table near him. He was going to cut up the picture and destroy it.

Suddenly Dorian ran across the room and pulled the knife from Basil's hand. 'Don't, Basil! Don't destroy the painting.

*Suddenly Dorian ran across the room and pulled the knife
from Basil's hand.*

It would be murder. Don't. . . please. . .'

'Well, I'm happy that you like the picture now, Dorian,' said Basil. 'When the paint is dry you can have your portrait.

'Now,' he continued, 'shall we have some tea?'

Basil rang a bell and soon his servant brought the tea. The three friends drank their tea quietly, then Harry spoke.

'Let's go to the theatre this evening,' he said.

'I don't think I want to go to the theatre,' answered Basil.

'I would like very much to go to the theatre with you, Lord Henry,' said Dorian quickly.

'Don't go, Dorian,' said Basil. 'Stay here and have dinner with me.'

'I can't, Basil. I want go to the theatre with Lord Henry,' said Dorian.

Harry listened and smiled. He knew Dorian would go with him.

4

Sibyl Vane

Harry did not know much about Dorian Gray. Basil had told Harry very little about the young man. But Harry wanted to know all about Dorian. So Harry asked his friends in London about Dorian Gray. He asked about Dorian's family.

Harry enjoyed the story of Dorian Gray. It was a sad and romantic story about love and death.

Dorian's grandfather was Lord Kelso, a very rich old man. Dorian's mother was Lord Kelso's daughter, the beautiful Lady Margaret. Lady Margaret fell in love when she was very young.

She ran away from home and married a soldier. But she did not have a happy life.

Lord Kelso was very angry and never talked to Lady Margaret again. Dorian's father, the soldier, was killed before Dorian was born. Lady Margaret died before Dorian was a year old. So Dorian was an orphan.

Harry was very pleased with the story of Dorian Gray. He knew that Dorian was beautiful and young. Now he also knew that Dorian was an orphan. And he knew that Dorian was going to be very rich. Soon Dorian would be twenty-one. Then he would have all Lord Kelso's money.

Yes – it was a sad and romantic story. Now Harry was even more interested in Dorian Gray.

Harry saw Dorian many times in the next few weeks. They met in people's houses and at art galleries and in theatres. Harry wanted to talk to Dorian. Dorian had listened to Harry in Basil's studio. Harry wanted the young man to listen to him again and again. He wanted to give his thoughts and ideas to the young man.

So Harry talked and talked – at the theatre and at parties and at dinners. He laughed, and played games with words. He said funny things. He said clever things. And he said dangerous things.

Everybody listened to Harry. But Harry was not talking to everybody. He was talking to Dorian. Sometimes Dorian smiled. Sometimes his eyes were wide open with surprise. Dorian listened to everything Harry said.

———

It was a month after Harry had met Dorian at Basil's studio. Harry had been out to lunch and he arrived home in the middle of the afternoon.

'You're very late, Harry,' said a voice. 'I've been waiting a long time to see you.' The voice sounded very unhappy. Harry went into the library.

'You're very late, Harry,' said Dorian again. 'I wanted to see you. I've got something to tell you. I'm in love, Harry. I have to tell you. I'm in love with the most beautiful girl.'

There was silence. Then Harry said, 'Who are you in love with?'

'With an actress,' answered Dorian. His face became red.

'Oh, Dorian,' Harry said, sitting down, 'all young men fall in love with actresses.'

'Don't say that, Harry. You haven't seen her.'

'Who is she?'

'Her name is Sibyl Vane.'

'I've never heard of her.'

'She isn't well known yet,' said Dorian. 'But everybody will know about her soon. One day she will be famous. She is a wonderful actress.'

'Oh, is she?' said Harry, lying back in his chair. 'Tell me about Sibyl Vane. Where did you meet her?'

'I will tell you about her, Harry. But you must be kind to me. You mustn't laugh at me. I met her because of you.'

'Because of me?' said Harry.

'Yes. You told me to find out about life. You told me to enjoy life – the good things and the evil things.

'So I went out. I walked around London. There was excitement and danger everywhere. I knew that something wonderful was going to happen.

'Then one night, I went to a different part of London. I had not been there before. At about half past eight, I was in front of a dirty little theatre. The manager was standing outside. He was a horrible man. He was fat and dirty. "It's a pound for a ticket, sir," he said. "Buy a ticket for the best seat in the theatre, sir." And he took his hat off. . .'

Dorian stopped speaking because Harry had started to laugh.

'Don't laugh at me, Harry,' he said. 'It's cruel of you to laugh at me. I'm telling you how I met Sibyl . . .

'The play was *Romeo and Juliet* by Shakespeare,' Dorian went on. 'Romeo was a fat, ugly old actor. But Juliet was a beautiful young actress. She was about seventeen years old. Her hair was dark brown. Her face was small and pale – like a little flower. Her eyes were large and dark blue. I fell in love with her immediately.

'I have been to that theatre every night for three weeks. I have seen Sibyl act in lots of different plays. She is a wonderful actress. Why didn't you tell me about actresses?'

'Because everybody falls in love with actresses, Dorian,' said Harry.

'You *are* cruel, Harry. I wish I had not told you about Sibyl.'

'You had to tell me about Sibyl,' answered Harry. 'You will always tell me everything that you do. Now tell me more.'

'Oh Harry,' said Dorian, 'Sibyl is wonderful. She calls me Prince Charming.'

Harry laughed, but he was pleased. Dorian had been a quiet, frightened boy when they met at Basil's studio. Now he was growing into a man, and learning about life.

'Harry, I want you to see Sibyl. I want you to see her act in *Romeo and Juliet.*'

'Very well, Dorian. I shall come tomorrow, and I shall bring Basil too.'

'Oh, Basil – yes. I'm afraid I haven't seen him for a week. He sent me my portrait and I haven't thanked him.

'I do like the picture, Harry,' Dorian continued. 'I am pleased with it, but it stays young and beautiful while I grow older. Today I am a whole month older than the picture.'

Harry smiled. 'We will see you tomorrow night at seven o'clock at the theatre,' he said.

Dorian left the house and Harry sat for a while in the library. He thought about Dorian.

Harry's brown eyes shone with pleasure. He was pleased that Dorian was in love. He wanted to see what Dorian did next. Harry did not care if Dorian was sad or happy. He had told Dorian to enjoy life – the good things and the evil things. And Harry was going to watch what Dorian did.

It was late and the sun was low in the sky. Harry got up from his chair and went to change his clothes. He went out to dinner.

When he returned home that evening, there was a telegram waiting for him. It said that Dorian was engaged to be married to Sibyl Vane.

5

Brother and Sister

'Mother, I am so happy,' whispered Sibyl Vane. 'I am very, very happy and I hope you are happy too.'

Mrs Vane did not look very happy. She was a small, thin woman who always looked tired. There was a lot of make up on her face and on her dry, thin mouth.

'Oh, Sibyl,' she said, 'you mustn't think about the young man who comes to the theatre. You must think about your acting. Mr Isaacs will be angry if you don't act well. He has given us a lot of money and you mustn't make a theatre manager angry.'

'I don't like Mr Isaacs, Mother, and I don't care about money,' replied Sibyl. 'I'm in love with Prince Charming.'

'Sibyl, Mr Isaacs gave us fifty pounds to pay our bills and buy clothes for James. You love James – you love your brother – don't you?' said Mrs Vane.

'Yes, of course I do,' replied Sibyl. 'But we have Prince Charming now. He will help us. We don't need Mr Isaacs.'

Sibyl Vane lived with her mother, and brother, James. They lived in London. But they lived in a small house in the north of London, a long way from Harry's large, expensive house.

It was the day after Sibyl had become engaged to Dorian. Sibyl and her mother were talking in their small living room.

'Sibyl,' said her mother, 'you are too young to fall in love. We don't know anything about this young man. I'm very worried about you. And you know James is going away tomorrow. I'm worried about James too. James is going away to Australia and you have fallen in love. What am I going to do?'

At that moment the door opened and James Vane came into the room. He was sixteen years old and he did not look like his sister. Sibyl was small and beautiful, with shining brown hair. James was large, with big hands and feet. His hair was dull and dark.

He smiled at Sibyl. 'Let's go for a walk,' he said. 'I want to talk to you.'

Sibyl went to get her coat and James spoke to his mother. 'I'm worried about Sibyl,' he said. 'I'm worried about the

21

young man who comes to see her every night at the theatre.'

'Don't worry, James,' Mrs Vane replied. 'Young men often fall in love with actresses. . .'

'But you don't know his name,' said James, angrily. 'Mother, you must take care of Sibyl.'

Sibyl and James went for a walk in Hyde Park. The park was busy. There were lots of people. There were people walking and people sitting in carriages pulled by horses.

Sibyl was happy. 'I think you will have a wonderful life in Australia, James. I think you will become rich. I think . . .'

She stopped speaking because James was not listening to her.

'Who is the young man who comes to see you?' he asked. 'Who is he? You don't know his name, do you?'

'I call him Prince Charming. And I love him. I will love him for ever. . .'

'You don't know his name,' James said again, angrily. 'He is a rich young man . . . and he will not marry you. He will –'

'Oh, look! Look, there he is! He's in that carriage!' Sibyl shouted.

She pointed across the park at a carriage. James looked across the park. But, at that moment, another carriage suddenly passed in front of the brother and sister. James never saw Prince Charming.

'Oh dear,' said Sibyl. 'I wanted you to see him.'

'I wanted to see him too,' replied her brother. 'Because I will kill him if he ever hurts you.'

At first Sibyl was angry with her brother. But she remembered that he was sixteen years old. He was a boy. He had never been in love.

'You won't hurt a man I love, will you, James?' she said.

'Oh, look! Look, there he is! He's in that carriage!'
Sibyl shouted.

'No, I won't,' he said at last. 'I won't hurt him if you love him.'

'I will always love Prince Charming,' said Sibyl. 'And he will always love me.'

So Sibyl and James were friends again. But that evening, James spoke again to their mother.

'If this young man hurts Sibyl,' he said. 'I will find him and I will kill him. I will kill him like a dog!'

6

At the Theatre

The same evening, Harry, Basil and Dorian went to the theatre. Basil was unhappy that Dorian was going to marry an actress. But he could see that Dorian was happy.

Mr Isaacs, the theatre manager, met the three friends outside the dirty little theatre. Dorian thought he was a horrible man. But Harry liked him.

Inside the theatre, it was very hot and the lights were bright. There was an orchestra, playing some music very badly. Lots of young men and women were laughing and shouting at each other. Harry looked around the dirty, noisy theatre. 'What a strange place to meet the person you love!' he said unkindly.

But Basil spoke kindly to Dorian. 'Yes, it is a strange place,' he said. 'But I'm pleased you came here. Sibyl has made you very happy.'

'Oh yes,' said Dorian. 'I'm sorry the orchestra is so bad,' he added. 'But soon you will see Sibyl.'

A few minutes later, the play started. And very soon things started to go wrong. Sibyl Vane was very lovely, but she acted very badly. Tonight she was a terrible actress.

The audience started to shout at the actors. Some people left the theatre. The manager looked very angry. Basil and Harry did not want to watch the play. And Dorian's face became very pale.

Harry picked up his coat and stood up. 'She is very beautiful, Dorian,' he said. 'But she can't act. Let's go.'

'I'm sorry I asked you to come with me,' said Dorian.

'Perhaps Sibyl is ill,' Basil said kindly. 'We'll come again another time.'

'No,' replied Dorian, 'she's not ill. Last night she was a great actress. Tonight, she is a very bad actress. She is a very ordinary person.'

'Don't talk like that!' cried Basil. 'She is the girl you love! Come with us, Dorian. Let's go.'

But Dorian would not leave the theatre. 'Go away and leave me here,' he said. 'I want to be alone.'

Basil and Harry left the theatre. The play became worse and worse. Most of the people left the theatre and went home.

When the play ended, Dorian went to see Sibyl. He went to her room behind the stage. He was very unhappy and angry. He had told Harry and Basil that Sibyl was a great actress. They had come to see her and tonight she had been a terrible actress.

But, when Dorian saw Sibyl, she looked pleased. She spoke to him happily. 'Oh, my dear, I acted very badly tonight.

'Before I met you I was a good actress. I pretended to be in love when I acted the part of Juliet. Now I don't need to act. I *am* in love. I don't want to act again. Isn't it wonderful!

You must take me away from the theatre. We must go away together.'

But Dorian did not look at her. He ran to a big armchair. He sat down and put his head on his arms. 'You have killed my love for you,' he whispered. 'I thought you were a great actress. You acted the parts of beautiful women. I loved you because you were clever and exciting. Now you are boring and stupid.'

'You don't mean this, do you?' whispered Sibyl.

'My God, I was stupid to love you,' said Dorian.

'Oh, tell me that you love me,' cried Sibyl. 'Kiss me. I will do anything for you! I will act again. I will be a good actress for you!'

Sibyl fell to the floor and she lay there, crying.

Dorian looked at her for a moment. Then he spoke. 'I am going now,' he said quietly. 'I don't want to be unkind to you, but I don't want to see you again.'

Dorian left the theatre and Sibyl lay on the floor crying.

7

Things Are Changing

It was late when Dorian left Sibyl and the theatre, but he did not go home. That night Dorian walked around London for hours. He did not care where he went. He was upset, angry and confused. The sun was rising when he went home.

Dorian decided to go to bed and went slowly towards his bedroom. He walked along the hall and through the library. Basil's portrait of Dorian was on a wall in the library. Suddenly Dorian stopped and looked at the portrait.

He was surprised. The painting looked different. The face in the painting had changed. Yes, it had changed!

Quickly, Dorian opened the curtains. Sunlight came into the room. Dorian looked closely at the picture and saw that the face was different. It looked unkind and cruel.

A huge mirror hung on another wall. Dorian looked in the mirror at his own face. He saw a beautiful young man. He had not changed. What had happened to the picture?

Suddenly Dorian remembered the day that Basil finished the picture. Dorian remembered his wish. He remembered his own words. 'I wish that I could always be young. I wish that the picture could grow old instead of me. I would give anything and everything for this to happen. I would give my soul!'

Why did the face in the picture look cruel and unkind? Was his wish coming true? Was the picture changing?

Dorian thought about Sibyl. Had he been cruel to Sibyl? He had left her lying on the floor, crying.

Yes, he had been cruel. But Sibyl had killed his love for her. He would not think about Sibyl again.

The face in the picture looked at him. In Basil's studio, the picture had shown Dorian that he was a beautiful young man. Now the picture showed Dorian that he was unkind and cruel.

Dorian was sure now – the picture was going to get older and he was going to stay young. The picture was going to become old and wrinkled and ugly and Dorian was not going to change. He was sorry for the picture.

And suddenly he was sorry for Sibyl. He looked at the cruel face in the picture. And he decided to be kind to Sibyl. He decided to marry her. He would never see Lord Henry Wotton again and he would marry Sibyl.

Dorian quickly covered the picture with a cloth and left the library.

Later that day, Dorian woke up after a long sleep. It was a quarter past one in the afternoon.

Dorian got dressed and went to the library. A servant brought him some food and also brought Dorian a letter. The letter had come from Harry that morning. Dorian looked at the envelope for a long time, then decided not to open it. He was never going to see Harry again.

Then Dorian looked at the cloth which was covering the portrait. Had the picture changed?

At first Dorian did not want to look at the picture again. Then he thought about Basil. What was he going to say to Basil? Perhaps Basil would want to see the picture again.

So Dorian locked the door of the library and slowly pulled the cloth off the picture.

The face on the picture looked unkind and cruel. It *had* changed. Dorian was horrified.

Dorian was frightened too. He had wished that he could stay young. He had wished that the picture could grow old. His wish was coming true. But the picture was showing Dorian that he was evil.

He decided again to be kind to Sibyl. He decided again to marry her. Then the picture would show that he was good and kind.

Dorian went to a table, sat down and started to write. He wrote to Sibyl. He wrote her a wonderful love-letter. He said he was sorry. He asked her to marry him. When he had finished the letter Dorian felt happy again.

8

Dorian Learns about Himself

Suddenly there was a knock on the door of the library.

'Dorian,' shouted Harry's voice. 'Dorian, are you there? Let me in, my dear boy. I want to see you.'

At first Dorian did not answer. He did not want to talk to Harry. Harry was a bad influence on him. Harry made him behave badly and think about strange things.

Dorian remembered Harry's words. 'You must do everything you want to do. You must enjoy life – the good things and the evil things. You must not worry about what other people think.'

But Harry was wrong. Dorian wanted to forget Harry's words now. He wanted to be good and kind to people.

Then Dorian decided to see Harry. He decided to talk to Harry for the last time. Dorian covered the picture with the cloth and unlocked the door of the library.

'Oh, Dorian,' said Harry, 'I am very sorry about what has happened. But don't worry about it. Don't think about it.'

'Are you talking about Sibyl?' asked Dorian.

'Yes,' replied Harry, 'but don't worry. Tell me, did you talk to Sibyl after the play last night?'

'Yes I did,' said Dorian. 'I was very angry with her. I was unkind and cruel to her. I can be cruel. Before last night I did not know I could be cruel. Now I have learnt more about myself.'

'I am pleased that you are not upset,' said Harry.

'I have decided what to do now,' replied Dorian. 'I have decided to be good and kind. I don't want to be cruel and evil. I am going to marry Sibyl.'

'Marry Sibyl? Dorian, didn't you read my letter? I wrote to you this morning. . .' Harry stopped speaking.

'No, I didn't,' said Dorian. 'I didn't want to read it. You are a bad influence on me.'

Harry walked across the room. He sat down next to Dorian and took hold of the young man's hands.

'Dorian, I'm sorry. That letter told you that Sibyl is dead.'

'Dead!' shouted Dorian. 'No! She isn't dead. She can't be dead. You're lying.' He pulled his hands away from Harry.

'It is true,' said Harry. 'The story is in all the newspapers. There is going to be an inquest – an inquiry to find out about her death. The police need to find out what happened.'

'Why? Why will there be an inquest? What happened?' Dorian shouted.

Then suddenly he stopped shouting and looked at Harry. 'She killed herself, didn't she? Tell me, Harry. Tell me quickly.'

'Yes. Sibyl didn't arrive home after the play. Her mother went to the theatre at about midnight. Sibyl was dead, lying in her room. She had drunk some poison.'

'Harry, Harry, this is terrible!' cried Dorian.

'Did anyone see you with Sibyl?' continued Harry. 'We don't want your name in the newspaper stories too.'

'No, nobody saw me,' replied Dorian quietly.

'Good,' said Harry. 'Now, you must come out with me tonight. There is a wonderful singer at the opera tonight.'

'So,' whispered Dorian to himself. 'I have killed Sibyl Vane. I did not cut her throat with a knife, but I killed her.'

Then Dorian remembered his portrait. He remembered the cruel face.

'I was going to be good and kind,' he shouted. 'I was going to marry Sibyl. Now I can never be good.'

Harry took a cigarette out of a gold case. 'It wasn't a good idea to decide to marry Sibyl,' he replied. 'You know it wasn't a good idea, don't you, Dorian? Marriage is boring. Marriage doesn't make you a good person.'

'Perhaps you are right,' said Dorian. 'I don't want to cry. Sibyl's death has been an interesting experience. I have learnt about myself. Now we do not need to talk about it again. I will meet you at the opera tonight.'

Harry left the library and Dorian went straight to the portrait. He quickly pulled away the cloth. The face was cruel and unkind. He knew the face had changed because of Sibyl's death.

Dorian thought about what had happened. And now he made a decision. Dorian decided to enjoy his life. He decided to do everything he wanted to do. He decided not to care about other people.

And Dorian knew what would happen. The picture would become old and wrinkled and ugly. *He* would always look young and beautiful. Dorian smiled and covered the picture with the cloth again.

An hour later, Dorian was at the opera with Harry.

Dorian went straight to the portrait. He quickly pulled away the cloth.

9

Secrets

The next morning, Dorian ate his breakfast in the library as usual. A servant came in while he was eating.

'Mr Hallward is here, sir,' the servant said.

Basil came quickly into the room behind the servant.

'I am very pleased to see you,' said Basil. 'I have been very worried about you. I came here last night after I read the news about Sibyl. Your servant said that you had gone to the opera, but I knew it couldn't be true.'

Dorian continued eating his breakfast.

'I thought you had gone to visit Sibyl's family,' Basil went on. 'I didn't know where you were.'

'My dear Basil,' said Dorian, 'I was at the opera of course.' Dorian sounded very bored. 'I had a nice evening. Now, don't talk about boring subjects. And don't talk about the past.'

'That is a terrible thing to say!' said Basil. 'The girl you love is dead and you tell me you had a *nice* evening! Yesterday is not the past. Yesterday is a few hours ago.'

'Stupid, boring people cannot forget the past quickly,' answered Dorian angrily. 'But I have forgotten it already.'

'The boy whose picture I painted was gentle and kind,' said Basil sadly. 'You have changed, Dorian. It is Harry's fault.'

'Oh, Basil,' said Dorian. 'You have come too late. Yesterday, when Harry told me Sibyl had killed herself . . .'

'Perhaps Sibyl didn't mean to kill herself,' said Basil. 'Perhaps it was an accident.'

'She wanted to kill herself,' answered Dorian. 'It wasn't a boring, ordinary accident. Sibyl's death was exciting and wonderful. She died of love for me.'

'Oh no,' said Basil quietly.

Dorian went on speaking. 'I was sad, Basil. I was sad yesterday at about half past five. Now I'm not sad, so you don't need to worry about me. Be pleased that I am not sad.'

Basil sighed. He decided to say nothing else about Sibyl.

'I would like to paint another portrait of you,' said Basil.

'No!' shouted Dorian. 'No. That's impossible. You can't.'

Basil was very surprised. 'But Dorian, why not?' he asked. Then he saw that a cloth was covering his portrait of Dorian. 'And why have you covered the picture? It's the best portrait I've ever painted.'

Basil walked across the room towards the painting.

'No!' shouted Dorian. 'You mustn't look at it!'

'But Dorian, I want to show the picture in a gallery in Paris,' replied Basil. 'I want to see it.'

'You can't,' said Dorian. 'I will never speak to you again if you look at it.

'And –' Dorian thought quickly, 'you have changed your mind. Harry said that you didn't want to show the picture in a gallery. Why didn't you want to show it? Harry said there was a strange reason.'

'You will laugh at me if I tell you,' Basil answered. 'So I won't ask to see the picture again.'

Dorian laughed now. 'No, Basil, I want to know. Why didn't you want to show the picture?'

Basil sighed. He started to explain. He told Dorian what he had told Harry.

'When I met you I knew you were important. You became my dearest friend. I became a better artist because of you.

'But an artist shows his feelings in his pictures. I did not want people to know my feelings. So I did not want to show the painting in a gallery.

34

'Now I am not so worried. I don't mind if people see the picture.

'So, now I have told you,' said Basil. 'But you will not let me see the picture. You will not let me paint you again. And you will not give me a reason. You make me very sad.'

Dorian smiled. Basil was not going to find out the secret of the picture. 'We are still friends,' Dorian said, 'and I will come and have tea with you soon. That will be nice.'

As soon as Basil left, Dorian walked across the library to the portrait. Carefully, he folded the cloth very tightly around the painting. Nobody, he thought to himself, will ever see this again.

Dorian rang a bell to call a servant. 'Get someone to help you,' he said. 'Carry this picture upstairs to the top of the house. Put it in the small room in the attic.'

Dorian watched while two servants carried the painting up to the attic room. Then he locked the door and put the key in his pocket. It was the only key to that room.

It was five o'clock when Dorian went back to the library. He found that Harry had sent him a copy of the evening newspaper.

There was a report in the newspaper about the inquest on Sibyl's death. The report said that Sibyl had drunk poison by accident and killed herself. The report did not say anything about Dorian. Dorian threw away the newspaper.

Later, Dorian met Harry at a hotel to have dinner. They sat at a small, round table.

'I'm hungry,' said Dorian.

Harry smiled.

Dorian watched while two servants carried the painting up to the attic room.

PART TWO

10

Two Friends

It was a night in November. And it was the night before Dorian's thirty-eighth birthday. Seventeen years had passed since Dorian had locked the portrait in the attic room.

Late in the evening, Dorian was walking home through the streets of London. He had been to a dinner party at a friend's house. Dorian was alone and he was thinking about his life. He was thinking about the last seventeen years.

For many years people had heard strange and terrible things about Dorian Gray, but they did not believe these things. When he was twenty Dorian had been a beautiful young man. Now he was thirty-eight and he was still a beautiful young man. People thought he must be good and kind.

People were wrong. The strange and terrible things were true. Dorian was unkind and cruel. Dorian spent time in strange places and he knew evil men.

But only Dorian knew the secret of the picture. He often went up to the attic room. He unlocked the room and stood in front of the picture for hours.

The face of the man in the picture was ugly and wrinkled. The face was getting older and older, and it was very, very evil. The picture showed the evil inside Dorian Gray. It showed the evil in his soul.

Often Dorian looked at the picture, then looked in a mirror. He laughed when he saw his face in the mirror. It was young and beautiful. Dorian's wish had come true.

Dorian was thinking. He had been happy for many years. He had enjoyed his life. He had not cared about other people. Dorian had done the things Harry had told him to do.

Dorian was a rich man. He bought a house in the country. He bought valuable pictures and fine books and he bought beautiful furniture. He wore beautiful clothes and expensive jewellery. He always wore many rings on his fingers.

But now Dorian was worried. He was worried because he was not happy any longer.

Some people would not speak to him now. Some people would leave a room when he entered it. Some people told stories about the strange life of Dorian Gray.

And Dorian was worried that somebody would find out the truth. He was worried that somebody would see the portrait. Then everybody would find out that the stories were true. They would find out that he was an evil man.

Dorian was hurrying home to see his portrait now. Often, he left dinner parties early and hurried home to see his portrait. Sometimes he went on holiday, then hurried home to see his portrait.

It was eleven o'clock and it was a foggy night. Dorian saw very few people as he walked home.

He had nearly reached his house when a man walked past him. The man was walking very fast and carrying a suitcase.

Dorian recognised the man. It was Basil Hallward. Dorian did not want to talk to Basil, so he walked more quickly. But suddenly he heard Basil's voice.

'Dorian! Dorian, I'm pleased to see you!'

Dorian had to stop and turn round.

'I've been to your house,' continued Basil. 'I wanted to see you before I went to Paris. I'm leaving on the midnight train and I wanted to talk to you before I went. I'm going to the station now. You walked straight past me. Didn't you recognise me?'

'It's impossible to recognise anyone in this thick fog,' replied Dorian. 'It's difficult to recognise my own house.

'It's nice to see you, Basil,' he went on, 'but aren't you going to miss your train?'

'Oh no, I can get to the station in twenty minutes and I do want to talk to you,' Basil replied.

'I'm going to live in Paris for six months. I want to talk to you before I go.'

Dorian was not pleased to see Basil, but he invited him into the house. They went to the library. Dorian lay back in a large armchair.

'I hope you don't want to be serious,' he said. 'I don't like serious things, Basil.'

'I'm sorry, Dorian,' replied Basil quietly, 'but it is serious.'

'What do you want to say?' cried Dorian. 'I hope you don't want to talk about me. I'm tired of myself tonight. I want to be somebody else.'

But Basil *did* want to talk about Dorian.

'People are saying terrible things about you, Dorian,' he said.

'I don't care,' replied Dorian quickly. 'It's interesting to hear terrible things about other people. But it's boring to hear terrible things about myself.'

'*These* terrible things must interest you,' replied Basil. 'You must care what other people say about you.

'I don't believe anything that I hear about you,' he continued. 'I look at your beautiful face and I know you are not an evil man. A man's face shows the evil that is inside him. I am an artist and I know this.'

Dorian's face became very pale. He sat silently and stared at Basil.

11

The Picture of Dorian Gray

Outside it was very dark and very foggy. In the library it was very quiet. The room was lit by a small lamp on a table. Basil sat down and continued talking.

'Why don't people want to be your friends any more, Dorian?' he asked. 'The Duke of Berwick will not stay in the same room as you. Because of you, Sir Henry Ashton has left England for ever.

'And there are worse things,' he went on. 'A young soldier has killed himself. Adrian Singleton has disappeared. Lord Kent is very upset about his son. Nobody will talk to the Duke of Perth. . . Oh, Dorian, these people were your friends. What have you done to them?'

'Stop it, Basil!' shouted Dorian. 'I haven't done anything. It is not my fault if young men do stupid things.'

'I want to believe you,' said Basil sadly. 'But you *have* influenced your friends. You have made people do terrible things. What did you do to Harry's sister? Now no one will speak to her. Are you an evil man, Dorian?'

'Take care, Basil,' said Dorian. 'Do not say any more.' But Basil continued speaking. 'I told people that you were a good man. I said I knew you well. But do I know you well? I cannot see your soul. I do not know if there is good or evil inside you.'

'No,' said Dorian slowly, 'you cannot see my soul.' His body was shaking and his face was very pale.

Basil looked at Dorian's face. 'Nobody can see inside another man,' he said. 'Nobody can see another man's soul.'

Suddenly Dorian laughed. He gave a loud, unpleasant laugh.

'Come with me, Basil,' he said, picking up the lamp from the table. 'You have said enough about my soul. Tonight you shall see it.'

Dorian led Basil upstairs towards the room in the attic.

When they reached the door of the room, Dorian turned to Basil. 'Are you sure you want to come in?' he asked.

'Yes,' Basil said. But he was confused. What did Dorian mean? What was in the room?

Dorian laughed again and unlocked the door. They walked across the room. Dorian put the lamp on an old table. Then he pointed at the cloth which covered the picture.

'You think that nobody can see another man's soul,' he said.

'You're wrong. Pull away that cloth and you will see mine.'

Dorian's voice was hard and cruel.

'What are you talking about? Are you mad?' asked Basil.

Suddenly Dorian pulled away the cloth and Basil saw the picture.

He saw the terrible face in the picture smiling at him. It was the most awful face he had ever seen. Basil moved backwards, away from that cruel, evil face.

He could see that it was his painting. It was his painting of the blond, pale and beautiful young man. The hair was blond, the mouth was red and the eyes were blue. But the face was wrinkled and ugly. And it was evil.

Dorian watched Basil. He smiled unpleasantly.

'What does this mean?' said Basil at last.

'Don't you know what it means, dear Basil?' said Dorian. 'It means that my wish came true. Do you remember the day you finished this portrait? Do you remember the day I met Harry? Do you remember my wish?'

'Oh God!' whispered Basil. 'You wished that the picture would grow old. You wished that you would stay young . . . Oh no!'

'Oh yes,' said Dorian. 'And the portrait shows you the true Dorian Gray. It shows you my soul.'

Basil sat down suddenly on an old chair. He put his head in his hands. 'Oh God,' he said. 'Oh God. You must be very evil. You are more evil than anybody knows.'

Basil fell forwards so his head and arms were on the table. He did not want to look at the picture again.

'We must pray, Dorian,' he said. 'It is not too late.'

'It is too late,' replied Dorian. 'It's much too late to pray.'

Then suddenly Dorian became angry. He became angry with Basil. It was Basil's fault. Basil had painted the picture. He hated Basil.

Dorian looked at the terrible face in the picture. It was smiling at him and it was evil.

A knife was lying on the old table. Dorian picked up the knife and looked at Basil. Then he stabbed his friend with the knife. He pushed the knife into Basil's neck. Basil's head hit the table. And Dorian stabbed him again and again.

Basil made a terrible sound. He tried to breathe, but he could not. Blood came from his mouth.

It became quiet in the attic room. Dorian listened. He heard the sound of Basil's blood dripping onto the carpet. There was no other sound.

It became quiet in the attic room.

Dorian walked quietly across the room and looked out of the window. The fog had gone and London was quiet.

Dorian walked back across the room and picked up the lamp. He saw the dead thing lying across the table. It was so quiet, and its hands were very white.

Dorian left the room and locked the door behind him. He went back to the library. Dorian quickly put Basil's suitcase and coat in a cupboard.

People were hanged for murder – hanged by the neck until they were dead. Dorian did not want to be hanged. What was he going to do?

Nobody has seen me arrive home, Dorian thought. The servants are asleep. And Basil was going to go to Paris tonight. He was going to catch the midnight train.

Dorian soon decided what to do.

It was five past two in the morning. Quietly, Dorian left the house and shut the door behind him. Then he started to ring the doorbell.

After five minutes, his servant, Francis, opened the door.

'I'm sorry to wake you up,' said Dorian, 'but I forgot my front door key. What time is it?'

'Ten minutes past two, sir,' replied Francis, looking at the clock.

'Oh dear. I'm very late!' said Dorian. 'Did anybody call while I was out?'

'Yes sir,' replied Francis. 'Mr Hallward called. He waited for you until eleven o'clock, then he went away to catch a train.'

'Oh! I'm sorry I didn't see him. Did he leave a message?'

'Yes sir. He said he was going to Paris. He said he would write to you.'

'Thank you, Francis,' said Dorian, 'you can go to bed now.'

Dorian went back to the library. He had to think again. He

walked up and down the room for a quarter of an hour. Then he picked up a book and looked through a list of addresses. At last he found the right address: Alan Campbell, 152 Hertford Street. Yes, Alan Campbell was the man he needed.

12

Dorian Asks for Help

At nine o'clock the next morning Dorian was sleeping. He did not look like a man who had murdered a friend.

But when he woke up, Dorian remembered what had happened. He tried not to think about Basil. He thought for a long time about which clothes to wear. He put on his rings. Then he took them off and put on different rings.

Dorian ate his breakfast. But he could not forget Basil's body, sitting at the table in the attic room. Then, at last, he wrote two letters. He put one letter in his pocket. He told his servant to take the other letter to Alan Campbell's house.

Dorian went to the library. He lit a cigarette and tried not to think about Basil. He drew pictures. But they were pictures of Basil's face. He read poems. But the poems reminded him of Basil.

Poor Basil, he thought. What a horrible way to die! Dorian became frightened. He thought about Alan Campbell. Perhaps Alan Campbell would not come!

Alan Campbell was a very clever scientist. Dorian and Alan Campbell had been good friends for many years. But Alan had not talked to Dorian for eighteen months. Nobody knew why they were not friends any more.

Now Dorian needed Alan's help.

At last Alan Campbell arrived. He had black hair and a very pale face. He looked very unhappy. Dorian was pleased to see him.

'Alan,' he said, shaking hands, 'it is kind of you to come. Thank you for coming.'

Alan did not look pleased to see Dorian. 'I did not want to come,' he said. 'I did not ever want to speak to you again. But your letter said it was very important – a matter of life and death.'

'Yes, it is very important,' said Dorian. Then he spoke very quickly. 'There's a dead man in a room upstairs. He's been dead for about ten hours. You must do something for me. You must.'

'I don't want to know anything about this!' said Alan Campbell. 'I won't do anything for you! Don't tell me your terrible secrets.'

'I must tell you this secret,' replied Dorian. 'You must help me. You are a scientist. You must destroy the body.'

'No, I will not,' said Alan Campbell. 'You are mad, Dorian. And I don't care what happens to you.'

The young man tried to leave the room, but Dorian stopped him. 'Alan,' he said, 'it was murder. I murdered this man and you are going to help me.'

Alan Campbell was horrified. He could not speak.

Dorian sat down and quietly wrote something on a piece of paper. Then he gave the paper to the young man.

Alan Campbell read what Dorian had written. His face became pale. His body started to shake. He fell down into a chair. There was silence.

'I am very sorry for you,' said Dorian sadly. 'We both know what you did. I do not want to tell anybody the truth about you.

But I will tell them if you don't help me. I have written a letter and I will send it . . .'

Dorian pulled the letter out of his pocket. He showed Alan the address on the envelope.

'Oh no!' whispered Alan Campbell. Then, very quietly, he spoke again. 'I must go home. I need some things from my house. I need some scientific equipment so I can help you.'

'You are not going to leave here,' said Dorian. 'Write a list and one of my servants will get the things you need.'

Sadly, Alan wrote the list. Soon Dorian's servant brought the scientific equipment from Alan's house. Then Dorian sent his servant away.

Alan Campbell and Dorian carried the equipment up to the attic room. There was a long piece of wire, two strange-shaped pieces of metal and a large wooden box with bottles in it.

Dorian unlocked the door and opened it. Basil's body was

sitting at the table. Dorian did not want to look. He did not want to go into the room again.

But suddenly Dorian saw that he had not covered the portrait again with the cloth. He ran across the room to cover the portrait.

And then he saw blood on the hands in the picture! Bright red blood! The picture was more horrible than Basil's body. Dorian pulled the cloth over the picture quickly and went back to the library. He left Alan Campbell to do his work.

Five hours later, Alan Campbell came into the library. His face was calm and pale.

'I have done what you asked me to do,' he said quietly. 'Goodbye. I never want to see you again.'

As soon as Alan had left, Dorian went upstairs. There was a strange and horrible smell in the attic room. But the terrible thing sitting at the table had gone.

13

Prince Charming

That evening Dorian dressed in beautiful clothes and went to a dinner party at a friend's house. But he did not enjoy the party and did not want to eat anything.

'Are you all right?' asked Harry. 'And were you all right last night? You left last night's party very early – about eleven o'clock.'

'Yes . . . no. I'm fine . . . I don't know what I did last night,' said Dorian quickly. 'Yes, I do. I went for a walk. I got home about two o'clock in the morning. I forgot my key. I had to wake the servant. You can ask him if you don't believe me.'

Dorian spoke quickly and sounded confused. Harry was surprised. 'My dear boy, I don't care what you did,' he said. 'Perhaps you are ill.'

'Yes,' replied Dorian, 'I'm not feeling well. I think I'll go home.'

When Dorian got home, he knew he had to do something terrible. He had to burn Basil's coat and suitcase, so that nobody would find out the truth about Basil's death. People thought Basil had gone to Paris. Nobody expected to see him for six months.

The coat and suitcase smelt horrible when he burnt them. Dorian felt very unhappy. He wanted to leave the house and forget everything.

At midnight, Dorian went out and found a cab. He told the cab driver quietly where he wanted to go.

The man shook his head. He looked frightened. 'It's too far. I can't go there at this time of night,' he said.

'Here's a pound for you,' said Dorian, 'and I'll give you another one if you drive fast.'

'All right, sir. We'll be there in an hour,' said the driver. Then he made the horse pull the cab fast along the streets. The cab went east – towards the River Thames.

It was another foggy, dark night in London. The light of street lamps shone through the fog. Cold rain began to fall. Men and women were walking home along the streets. Dorian heard screams and shouts and horrible laughter.

He sat back on the seat of the cab, watching. He hated London. He hated life. He wanted to forget everything. He wanted opium – the drug that would make him forget.

The cab drove on through dirty, poor parts of the city. Near the river the fog disappeared. Dorian left the cab and walked towards the river. The moon was shining on the water. The ships on the river were big and black. The light from street lamps shone down onto the wet road.

Soon he reached a small, dirty house. Inside the house it was dark. A dirty green curtain hung over a doorway. Dorian went through the doorway and into a long room.

A few men were drinking. A sailor, half-asleep, lay with his head on a table. Two women were arguing. Dorian went through this room and up some stairs to another one. He could smell opium and he smiled with pleasure. Now he could smoke some opium and forget everything.

But then Dorian saw a young man smoking a pipe full of opium. Immediately, Dorian recognised him. It was Adrian Singleton, who had been a friend of Dorian's. 'Adrian Singleton has disappeared,' Basil had said. But here was Adrian, in an opium den.

Dorian went quickly back to the first room. He did not want to see anyone he knew. He would go to another opium den. As he went back through the green curtain a voice called after him. One of the women was shouting.

'Look at him! There he is – Prince Charming!'

Suddenly the sailor lifted his head from the table.

'Don't talk to me!' shouted Dorian angrily to the woman.

And he ran out of the house. Dorian turned a corner into a narrow, dark street. He was running to another opium den. He was trying to forget about Adrian Singleton.

Suddenly a strong hand was round Dorian's neck. 'Keep quiet or I'll shoot you!' said a voice.

Dorian turned round and saw a gun pointing at his head. He saw a large man, a sailor. 'Are you mad?' Dorian said. 'What have I done to you?'

'My sister is dead because of you!' replied the sailor. 'Sibyl Vane killed herself and now I'm going to kill you. I have looked for you for years. And tonight I heard the name she called you.'

Dorian was afraid. He looked at James Vane and could not move. This man was going to kill him.

Then suddenly Dorian had an idea. 'How long is it since your sister died?' he asked.

'Seventeen years. Why do you ask?' replied the man.

'Look at me! Look at me by the light of a street lamp,' said Dorian.

James Vane pulled Dorian back to the main street. And in the light of a street lamp, he saw the face of a beautiful young man. It was the face of a young man of about twenty.

'You can't be the man,' said James Vane. 'My God, I was going to murder you. I'm very sorry, sir.'

'You must be more careful,' Dorian said. Then he walked away round the corner and into the darkness.

As soon as Dorian had gone, the woman from the opium den ran up to the sailor. 'Why didn't you kill him?' she asked. 'He's evil.'

'He's not the man I want,' he replied. 'The man I want is about forty. That young man was twenty.'

The woman gave a horrible laugh. 'Twenty! Him? Prince Charming? I first saw Prince Charming seventeen years ago. But he hasn't changed since then.'

'You're lying!' shouted James Vane.

'I'm not,' said the woman. 'He was a beautiful young man seventeen years ago. And he hasn't changed since then. He's evil, that one!'

'Swear to God that you're not lying!'

In the light of the street lamp, James Vane saw the face of a beautiful young man.

'I swear I'm not lying,' the woman replied.

James Vane believed her. He ran round the corner into the narrow, dark street. But Dorian had gone.

14

Dorian Learns about Fear

A week later, Dorian was at his house in the country. Many people had come to stay with him. They were rich people who enjoyed talking and eating and drinking. Dorian's guests also enjoyed shooting – shooting birds and animals.

One evening, Dorian was with Harry and another friend, Lady Monmouth. Harry was laughing and saying clever things as he usually did. Lady Monmouth was laughing and listening to Harry. Dorian was listening too.

'I must leave you now,' said Lady Monmouth. 'I want to change my dress before we have dinner.'

'Let me get you some flowers. You can wear them on your dress,' said Dorian getting up from his chair and leaving the room.

'Oh,' said Lady Monmouth, 'I hope he gets me flowers that will look right with the colour of my dress.'

'Let's follow him,' replied Harry, 'and you can tell him the colour of your dress.'

As they left the room, Harry and Lady Monmouth suddenly heard a crash.

In the next room they found Dorian. He was lying on the floor next to a window. He had fainted.

Dorian soon opened his eyes, but his body was shaking and his face was very pale.

'Are you ill, dear boy?' asked Harry. 'You fainted. You must go and lie down.'

'No,' said Dorian quickly. 'I don't want to lie down. I don't want to be alone.'

So Dorian had dinner with his guests. He talked and laughed with them. He made jokes and told stories.

But he was remembering the white face looking at him through the window. It had been the face of James Vane!

The next day Dorian would not leave his bedroom. He felt ill and he was frightened. He was frightened if he heard a noise or saw a door open.

He remembered Sibyl Vane. He remembered the murder of Basil. He remembered the face at the window.

Dorian lay in bed, but he did not sleep. During the day, Harry went into Dorian's room and found Dorian crying.

After two days Dorian was not so frightened. James Vane could not know where he was. James Vane must be in London. He had imagined James Vane's face at the window.

On the third day Dorian was feeling better. Some of his guests were going out to shoot birds and Dorian decided to go too.

It was a cold day and the sun was shining. Dorian felt happy as he walked through the woods. Harry and Lady Monmouth walked beside him.

Suddenly one of the guests shot at something among the trees. There was a cry – the terrible cry of a man in pain.

People shouted and ran towards the noise. Soon they pulled the body of a man out of the trees. Dorian watched in horror.

Soon they pulled the body of a man out of the trees.
Dorian watched in horror.

Harry touched Dorian's arm. 'I think we'd better stop shooting today,' he said.

'Oh Harry, this is terrible and something more terrible is going to happen. I know it,' replied Dorian.

'Don't worry about it, Dorian,' said Harry. 'It was an accident. It wasn't a murder.'

Harry was never serious for long. 'I would like to meet a person who has done a real murder,' he went on, laughing.

Lady Monmouth laughed too, but Dorian suddenly felt ill. His face became very pale.

Dorian smiled politely. 'I'm feeling tired. I must go to my room. Excuse me.'

In his room, Dorian lay down on his bed. His body shook with terror. Fear and death were everywhere in this house. He did not want to spend another night here.

At five o'clock Dorian told his servant that he wanted to take the night train to London. The servant went to pack Dorian's suitcases, but he soon returned.

'Excuse me, sir,' he said to Dorian, 'there is a problem with the dead man, the man who was shot.'

'Yes, what is it?' said Dorian. 'Do you need money to give to his family?'

'No, sir. This is the problem. We don't know who he is. He was carrying some money and a gun. But we could not find his name on anything. He's a sailor . . .'

'A sailor!' cried Dorian. Suddenly he was excited and hopeful. He ran to the door. 'Where is the body? Quick! I want to see it now!'

The body had been taken to a farm. It lay on the floor in one of the buildings. A handkerchief covered the dead man's face.

'Take that cloth off the face,' said Dorian.

A farm-worker took away the handkerchief. Then Dorian looked down at the face and gave a cry of joy. The man who had been shot was James Vane.

Dorian went home with his eyes full of tears. They were tears of joy because he was safe. James Vane could not kill him now.

15

A New Start for Dorian?

One evening in June, Dorian was visiting Harry. Harry and Dorian sat in Harry's library.

'Harry, I have done too many terrible things in my life,' said Dorian. 'Yesterday I started to change my life. I'm going to be good.'

Harry smiled. 'Where were you yesterday?' he asked.

'I was at an inn in a small village,' replied Dorian.

'What did you do at this inn?' asked Harry, laughing. 'How did you start to be good?'

'I met a girl,' said Dorian. 'She was a pretty girl called Hetty. She looked like Sibyl Vane.

'Hetty and I were going to go away together,' Dorian went on. 'But I decided not to go away with her. I decided to leave her in her village. I have done something good.'

'You are pleased because you have done something good,' said Harry. 'But she will kill herself because you left her.'

'Don't say that! You are never serious,' said Dorian angrily.

'You wanted to be good, so you left her,' replied Harry. 'You did what you wanted to do. You haven't changed.'

Harry was right.

Dorian did not want to talk about Hetty again. 'Have you got any news?' he asked.

'No, there is nothing else to talk about,' replied Harry. 'People are talking about Basil. Nobody knows what has happened to him.'

'Basil!' said Dorian, in a surprised voice. 'Are people still talking about him? It's a month since people noticed that he had not come back from Paris!'

'My dear boy, people will talk about Basil for three months. Then they will talk about somebody else. They will talk about Alan Campbell's death too. He killed himself, you know.'

Dorian did not want to talk about Alan Campbell. But he talked about Basil.

'What do you think happened to Basil, Harry?'

'I don't know. Perhaps he is dead. I don't want to think about it,' replied Harry.

There was silence for a while, then Dorian spoke again.

'People are saying that Basil was murdered, aren't they? Do you think Basil was murdered?'

'Nobody would want to murder Basil,' replied Harry. 'Everybody liked Basil. He didn't have any enemies.'

'Perhaps I murdered Basil,' said Dorian. 'Have you thought of that, Harry?' Dorian watched Harry carefully.

But Harry laughed. 'You're talking nonsense, dear boy. You couldn't murder anybody.

'Let's talk about something else,' Harry continued. 'Poor Basil isn't interesting any more. He hadn't painted a good picture for a long time. What happened to his picture of you, Dorian?'

'Oh, I lost it,' replied Dorian quickly.

'You look the same now – as young as you were when the picture was painted,' said Harry. 'Don't change your life. You

58

have had a good life. You have done everything you wanted to do and you have not changed at all.'

'I'm not the same as that young man,' said Dorian. 'I want to change. I want to be good.'

'Don't change,' said Harry. 'You are beautiful and you are perfect. You and I will always be friends.'

As he left Harry's house, Dorian's face was very sad.

It was a warm night. Dorian started to walk home from Harry's house. He walked past two young men and heard one of them whisper, 'That's Dorian Gray.'

Dorian felt tired. He did not want people to recognise him. He did not want people to talk about him any longer. He did not want to hear his name.

As he walked, Dorian thought about his life. Dorian suddenly wanted to be young again. He wanted to be the young man whose picture Basil had painted.

Dorian was still thinking when he reached home.

Perhaps it was not too late to change his life. He had been kind to Hetty. He had left her in her village. Perhaps he was starting to be good.

Dorian went up to the attic room. He wanted to look at the picture. Perhaps the picture was changing again. Perhaps the picture was not so ugly now. Perhaps the cruel, evil face was changing and becoming kinder.

But the face in the picture was the same. It was old and wrinkled and ugly. The eyes were cruel. The mouth was evil. The blood was still on the hands.

When Dorian saw the picture, he knew the truth. He knew that he could never change. He would always be evil.

There was a knife on the table in the attic room. He had used that knife to kill Basil.

Dorian picked up the knife. It had killed Basil and now it

would kill his painting. Then nobody would ever know that Dorian Gray was an evil man!

———

There was a loud crash and a cry. It was a loud and horrible cry which woke the servants.

There were two men in the street outside and they heard the cry too.

'Whose house is this?' asked one of the men.

'Dorian Gray's,' replied the other man.

The two men looked at each other in horror, then they quickly walked away.

Inside the house, it was now quiet. The door of the attic room was locked, but at last the frightened servants opened it.

Inside the room they found a picture hanging on a wall. It was a picture of their master, Dorian Gray. He looked young and beautiful in the picture. He looked the same as he had always looked.

On the floor they found a man. He was ugly and old and wrinkled. His face was evil. And he was dead, with a knife in his heart.

At first the servants did not know the man.

But then they looked at the rings on his fingers and they knew who it was.

Points for Understanding

1

1 What are the names of the two people in the artist's studio? What do you know about each of these people?
2 The artist is painting a portrait. He does not want to show this portrait in an art gallery. Why not?
3 The artist does not want his friend to meet the young man. Why?

2

1 What does Dorian Gray look like?
2 Lord Henry Wotton tells Dorian how to live his life. What does he tell him?
3 Lord Henry tells Dorian, 'You mustn't get burned by the sun.' Why does he say this?

3

1 How does Dorian feel when he first looks at the portrait?
2 Dorian remembers what Harry said in the garden. How does Dorian feel about the portrait now?
3 Dorian makes a wish. What does he wish?
4 Basil says, 'You have made me hate my best painting.'
   (a) What does Basil decide to do?
   (b) What does Dorian do?

4

1 Harry sees Dorian many times in the next few weeks. What does Harry do and why?
2 Dorian tells Harry that he has fallen in love. Who has Dorian fallen in love with?
3 What do Harry and Dorian arrange to do the next night?
4 Harry gets a telegram. What does the telegram tell him?

5

1 Why is Mrs Vane worried about Sibyl and James?
2 Why is James angry with Sibyl?
3 What does Sibyl call Dorian?
4 Why does James wish that he had seen Dorian in the park?

6

1 What goes wrong at the theatre?
2 What do Harry and Basil do?
3 After the play, Dorian goes to Sibyl's room. What does he do and say?

7

1 Dorian looks at the portrait. Why does he do this?
2 Why does Dorian suddenly remember the day that Basil finished the picture?
3 Dorian gets a letter from Harry. What does he do with it and why?
4 Why does he look at the picture again?
5 He decides to be kind to Sibyl. Why?

8

1 What was the news in Harry's letter?
2 Write down a sentence from page 30 and a sentence from page 31 to show how Dorian feels about this news.
3 Dorian makes a decision. What is this decision?

9

1 Why does Basil come to see Dorian?
2 Why doesn't Dorian want Basil to see the painting?
3 Why does Basil want to see the painting?
4 What does Dorian do after Basil leaves?

10

1 Seventeen years have passed.
    (a) What does Dorian look like now?
    (b) What does the picture look like now?
2 Dorian is no longer happy. Why isn't he happy?
3 Who does Dorian meet outside his house? Why has this person come to see him?

11

1 'Take care Basil,' said Dorian. 'Do not say any more.'
What has Basil been saying?

2   Why does Dorian take Basil upstairs to the room in the attic?
3   Suddenly Dorian becomes angry. What happens next?
4   Dorian leaves the house and shuts the front door behind him. Why does Dorian do this?

12

1   Dorian writes two letters. What does he do with each letter?
2   Who is Alan Campbell? What does Dorian ask him to do?
3   Dorian takes Alan to the attic room. What has happened to the picture?

13

1   Dorian leaves a party and goes home. What does he do next?
2   Why does Dorian go to the small, dirty house near the river?
3   'Keep quiet, or I'll shoot you,' says a voice.
      (a) Why has this person said this?
      (b) How has this person found Dorian?
4   What does the woman from the opium den tell the man about Dorian?

14

1   Where are Dorian and Harry staying?
2   Harry and Lady Monmouth suddenly hear a crash. What has happened and why?
3   Dorian and his guests go shooting. What happens?
4   Who is the dead man? Why is Dorian happy that this man is dead?

15

1   Does Harry know that Dorian killed Basil?
2   Why does Dorian go to look at the picture?
3   When Dorian saw the picture, he knew the truth. What is the truth?
4   Dorian picks up a knife. What happens next?
5   What do the servants find in the small attic room?

Exercises

People in the Story

Write the correct name next to each description below.

Sibyl Vane   Basil Hallward   James Vane   ~~Lord Henry~~   Dorian Gray

1	Lord Henry	He had a thin face and clever, dark eyes. His voice was slow and beautiful. People listened to him when he talked.
2		His face was pale and beautiful. His eyes were bright blue. His hair was blond.
3		He had black hair and a strong, intelligent face. He was a successful artist. He worked hard and painted many pictures.
4		She was small and beautiful, with shining brown hair. She worked as an actress.
5		He had large hands and feet. His hair was dull and dark. He became a sailor.

Nicknames

Lord Henry is called Harry in the story. Match these nicknames with the correct full name.

Mike   Kate   Dick   Lizzy   Sue

1	Catherine	
2	Michael	
3	Elizabeth	
4	Susan	
5	Richard	

Grammar Focus 1: *best ... ever*

Write full sentences using *best ... ever* and the prompts.

1   picture / you / paint
That is the best picture you have ever painted.

2   answer / you / give
That is

3   thing / you / do
That is

4   homework / you / do
That is

5   gift / he / buy
This is

6   story / you / tell
That is

7   cake / she / make
This is

8   party / they / have
That is

9   car / I / drive
That is

10 place / we / be
This is

11 meal / I / cook
That is

12 photos / take / She
These are

Grammar Focus 2: *wish*

We use *wish (that)** + *would/wouldn't* to talk about something which we would like to happen or something which we would like to be different from how it is.

Rewrite the sentences using *wish (that) + would/wouldn't*.

1   I want Basil to paint my portrait.
    I wish (that) Basil would paint my portrait.
    ....

2   I want Harry to leave my friends alone.

    ....

3   I don't want Sybil to act badly.

    ....

4   I hope Sybil will leave me alone.

    ....

5   I want Harry to tell me everything.

    ....

6   I don't want Dorian to be cruel to people.

    ....

7   I don't want you to talk about me.

    ....

8   I hope Lord Henry will help me.

    ....

9   I want the face in the portrait to stop getting old.

    ....

    ....

* *that* is used more in written than in spoken English.

Words From the Story

P	A	M	U	R	D	E	R	A	O
O	T	B	F	F	O	Y	I	R	P
R	H	B	L	A	B	A	S	T	I
T	E	L	B	S	M	A	R	I	U
R	A	O	D	C	R	O	G	S	M
A	T	N	T	T	T	X	U	T	H
I	R	D	A	C	T	R	E	S	S
T	E	R	I	N	G	S	O	U	L
S	D	D	O	S	T	A	B	S	A
K	R	A	S	T	U	D	I	O	Y

Find words in the square with the meanings below. The numbers in brackets show the number of letters in each word.

1 a woman who has parts in plays at the theatre (7)
   ACTRESS
   ....

2 a person who paints or draws pictures (6) ....

3 light-coloured (hair) (5) ....

4 known by many people (6) ....

5 the act of killing somebody deliberately (6) ....

6 a drug made from the seeds of a type of poppy (5) ....

7 a picture of a person (8) ....

8 circles of metal worn on the fingers (5) ....

9 the innermost part or spirit of a person or thing (4)

   ....

10 to pierce or kill with a knife (4) ....

11 a place where an artist works (6) ....

12 a place that shows plays (7) ....

Pronunciation

**In each group of words, only four have the same vowel sound.
Circle the odd one out.**

1	could	should	wood	good	(food)
2	cool	rude	blood	fool	mood
3	young	mud	but	put	love
4	door	book	cook	took	look
5	port	law	saw	fair	for
6	hair	bear	far	care	fare
7	dark	bare	park	part	mark
8	pure	fur	shirt	hurt	were
9	dear	meat	rear	fear	peer
10	feet	seat	heat	beat	great

A Chance Meeting with James Vane

Complete the gaps. Use each word in the box once.

face _out_ afraid move corner mad man kill looked street alone
dead herself idea since name twenty den followed around
quiet done lamp years light neck young murder turned gun

Dorian ran ¹.........._out_......... of the opium den. He turned a ².......................
into a narrow, dark ³................................. .

He was not ⁴................................. . Someone had ⁵...................................

68

him from the opium den. A strong hand closed [6].................................
Dorian's neck. 'Keep [7]........................... or I'll shoot you!' said a voice.
'Look at me!' The hand let go of Dorian's [8]................................. .
Dorian [9].......................... round and saw a [10].......................... pointing
at his head. He saw a large [11]..............................., a sailor.
'Are you [12].............................?' Dorian said. 'What have I
[13].......................... to you?'

'My sister is [14].................................. because of you!' replied the sailor.
'Sibyl Vane killed [15]....................................... and now I'm going to
[16].......................... you. I have [17]... for you for
years. And tonight I heard your [18].............................. in the opium
[19].............................. .'

Dorian was [20].. . He looked at James Vane and
could not [21].............................. . This man was going to kill him.
Suddenly Dorian had an [22].............................. . 'How long is it
[23].............................. your sister died?' he asked.

'Seventeen [24].............................. . You know that,' the man replied
angrily.

'Look at me! Look at me by the [25].................................. of a street
lamp,' said Dorian.

James Vane pulled Dorian back to the main street. And in the light of
a street [26].................................., he saw the [27].............................. of a
beautiful young man. It was the face of a [28].................................. man of
about [29].................................. .

'You can't be the man,' said James Vane. 'You're too young. My God, I
was going to [30].. you.'

Multiple Choice

Tick the best answer.

1 Why did Basil think that Lord Henry was a bad influence on people?

a ☑ Because he said things that changed people.

b ☐ Because he was a criminal.

c ☐ Because he smoked opium.

2 Why did Dorian change his mind about wanting to marry Sibyl Vane?

a ☐ Because she acted badly in the play one night and he no longer thought she was a special person.

b ☐ Because Harry did not think she was beautiful.

c ☐ Because he found out that she had no money.

3 What was strange about the picture of Dorian Gray?

a ☐ It changed and grew older while Dorian remained young.

b ☐ It faded very quickly.

c ☐ People thought that it was actually a photograph.

4 Why did Dorian ask his servants to put the portrait in the attic room?

a ☐ Because he had never liked it.

b ☐ Because he was getting older and he didn't like to look at a picture of himself when he was young and beautiful.

c ☐ Because the picture showed the truth about how evil he had become.

5 Basil had heard terrible things about Dorian Gray. Why didn't he believe them?

a ☐ Because he had never trusted other people.

b ☐ Because Dorian's beautiful face showed no evil.

c ☐ Because Dorian told him that they were not true.

6 Why did Dorian Gray kill Basil?
a ☐ Basil wanted to destroy the picture.
b ☐ Dorian hated Basil for painting the picture.
c ☐ Basil was going to tell the police about Dorian.

7 What is an opium den?
a ☐ A place where people drink gin at night.
b ☐ A secret place for smoking drugs.
c ☐ A place where gentlemen meet to play cards.

8 Why was Dorian frightened after he went to the opium den in London?
a ☐ Because he knew the police had seen him going there.
b ☐ Because he kept seeing Basil's ghost.
c ☐ Because he knew James Vane wanted to kill him.

9 Why did Dorian decide that he wanted to change?
a ☐ Because Harry told him he should.
b ☐ Because he wanted to be young and good again.
c ☐ Because he could only marry Hetty if he changed.

10 Why did Dorian Gray stab his own picture?
a ☐ Because he hated the evil in himself.
b ☐ Because he hated the artist.
a ☐ Because it reminded him of Basil.

11 How did the servants recognise the body of Dorian Gray?
a ☐ By his fine white teeth.
b ☐ By the clothes he was wearing.
c ☐ By the rings on his fingers.

12 Look back at the first activity (People in the Story). Which of the five characters was still alive at the end of the story?
a ☐ Dorian Gray.
b ☐ James Vane.
c ☐ Lord Henry.

Published by Macmillan Heinemann ELT
Between Towns Road, Oxford OX4 3PP
Macmillan Heinemann ELT is an imprint of
Macmillan Publishers Limited
Companies and representatives throughout the world
Heinemann is a registered trademark of Pearson Education, used under licence.

ISBN 978–0–230–02922–4
ISBN 978–1–4050–7658–6 (with CD pack)

This retold version by F. H. Cornish for Macmillan Readers
First published 1993
Text © F. H. Cornish 1993, 1998, 2002, 2005
Design and illustration © Macmillan Publishers Limited 2002, 2005

This edition first published 2005

Illustrated by Annabel Large
Original cover template design by Jackie Hill
Cover photography by Corbis/Roy McMahon

Printed in Thailand
2010 2009 2008
6 5 4 3 2

with CD pack
2012 2011 2010
15 14 13 12